Developing Nur

NUMBERS AND THE NUMBER SYSTEM

ACTIVITIES FOR THE DAILY MATHS LESSON

year

4

Hilary Koll and Steve Mills

A & C BLACK

Contents

Introduction   4

Place value, ordering and rounding (whole numbers)

Thousand and 1000	reading and writing whole numbers	7
Mix and match 1	reading and writing whole numbers	8
Mix and match 2	reading and writing whole numbers	9
What's it worth?	knowing what each digit represents	10
Tropical fish	knowing what each digit represents	11
Brick wall challenge	partitioning large numbers	12
Addition ladders	adding 1, 10, 100 and 1000 to any integer	13
Subtraction snakes	subtracting 1, 10, 100 and 1000 from any integer	14
Ten more, ten less	counting on or back in tens	15
Jumping in 100s	counting on or back in hundreds	16
Spot the patterns	counting on or back in thousands	17
Multiplication match	multiplying by 10	18
Division match	dividing by 10	19
Mystery numbers	multiplying and dividing by 10	20
Snake game	multiplying by 100	21
Crocodile maths	greater than/less than/equals	22
More, less or the same?	greater than/less than/equals	23
Stuck in the middle	numbers lying between two given numbers	24
Think of a number	ordering whole numbers	25
Where is it roughly?	estimating positions on a number line	26
The maths menace strikes	estimating quantities	27
Buzzing bees	rounding to the nearest 10	28
Round and round	rounding to the nearest 100	29
Roadhog	rounding to the nearest 10 or 100	30
Negative numbers	negative numbers in context	31
Getting warmer!	ordering temperatures	32

Properties of numbers and number sequences

Number nests	recognising and extending number sequences	33
River trail	counting in 25s	34
Crazy counting	counting in different-sized steps	35
Numbers on the line	counting in 11s	36
Pattern puzzles	counting in different-sized steps	37
Odd or even?	recognising odd and even numbers	38
Return of the maths menace	recognising odd and even numbers and their properties	39

| Counting sticks | recognising multiples of 2, 3, 4, 5 up to 10th multiple | 40 |
| Fairground hoopla | recognising multiples of 2, 3, 4, 5 up to 10th multiple | 41 |

Fractions and decimals

Parts of a whole	using fraction notation	42
Picture match	recognising mixed numbers	43
Fractions in the news	recognising mixed numbers	44
Equivalence match	recognising the equivalence of simple fractions	45
Fraction action game	identifying two simple fractions with a total of one	46
Ordering fractions	ordering a set of fractions	47
Dividing with fractions	relating fractions to division	48
Shrinking numbers	finding fractions of numbers	49
Fractions of measures	finding fractions of measures	50
Money matters	finding fractions of money	51
Fraction frenzy	finding the fraction that one unit is of another	52
Bargain buys	using ideas of simple proportion	53
One in every...	using ideas of simple proportion	54
Decimal birds	using decimal notation for tenths	55
What's the difference?	understanding decimal notation for tenths	56
Fish 'n' lines	ordering decimals with one decimal place	57
Money, money, money	ordering amounts of money	58
Pounds and pence	converting money from pounds to pence and vice versa	59
Centimetre centipede!	converting measurements to different metric units	60
The price is right	rounding sums of money to the nearest pound	61
Money puzzles	solving problems involving money and measures	62
Tipping the balance	understanding and comparing decimals with hundredths	63
Rabbits on the loose	recognising equivalence between decimals and fractions	64

Reprinted 2000, 2002
First published 2000 by A&C Black Publishers Limited
37 Soho Square, London W1D 3QZ
www.acblack.com

ISBN O-7136-5240-3

Copyright text © Hilary Koll and Steve Mills, 2000
Copyright illustrations © Gaynor Berry, 2000
Copyright cover illustration © Charlotte Hard, 2000

The authors and publisher would like to thank the following teachers for their advice in producing this series of books:
Tracy Adam; Shilpa Bharambe; Hardip Channa; Sue Hall; Ann Hart; Lydia Hunt; Madeleine Madden; Helen Mason;
Anne Norbury; Jane Siddons; Judith Wells; Fleur Whatley.

A CIP catalogue record for this book is available from the British Library.

Printed in Great Britain by St Edmundsbury Press Ltd, Bury St Edmunds, Suffolk.

Introduction

Developing Numeracy: Numbers and the Number System is a series of seven photocopiable activity books designed to be used during the daily maths lesson. The books focus on the first strand of the National Numeracy Strategy *Framework for teaching mathematics*. The activities are intended to be used during the time allocated to pupil activities; they aim to reinforce the teaching within the lesson and provide practice and consolidation of the objectives contained in the framework document.

Year 4 supports the teaching of mathematics to Year 4 children by providing a series of activities to develop and reinforce essential skills in number work. The activities relate to place value, ordering and rounding; properties of numbers and number sequences; and fractions and decimals. They build on the children's understanding of the concepts taught in Year 3 and also introduce –

- multiplying integers by 10 and 100, and dividing integers by 10;
- using symbols correctly, including greater than, less than and equals;
- recognising negative numbers in context;
- counting in steps of constant size, extending beyond zero when counting back;
- beginning to relate fractions to division;
- beginning to use ideas of simple proportion;
- understanding decimal notation;
- recognising equivalence between decimal and fraction forms.

Extension

Many of the activity sheets end with a challenge (**Now try this!**) which reinforces and extends the children's learning, and provides the teacher with the opportunity for assessment. Where children are asked to carry out an activity, the instructions are clear to enable them to work independently, although the teacher may wish to read out the instructions and provide further support where necessary. The children may need to write their answers on a separate piece of paper.

Organisation

For some of the activities, it will be helpful to have available coloured pencils, counters, scissors, number lines, place value cards (sometimes called arrow cards) and 100-squares. Several of the sheets involve cutting out cards, which can be done by the children themselves or by an adult before the lesson. To help teachers to select appropriate learning experiences for their children, the activities are grouped into sections within each book. The pages are not intended to be presented in the order in which they appear unless otherwise stated.

Teachers' notes

Very brief notes are provided at the end of most pages, giving ideas and suggestions for maximising the effectiveness of the activity sheets. These notes could be masked before photocopying.

Structure of the daily maths lesson

The recommended structure of the daily maths lesson for Key Stage 2 is as follows:

Start to lesson, oral work, mental calculation	5–10 minutes
Main teaching and pupil activities	about 40 minutes
Plenary	about 10 minutes

Each lesson should include:
- a pacey start with the whole class involved in counting, and oral and mental calculation work;
- some direct interactive teaching of the whole class on the maths objective for the day;
- group or individual activities linked to the objective of the lesson. The teacher should focus on one group to continue teaching directly. The activities in the **Developing Numeracy** books are designed to be carried out in the time allocated to group activities;
- a plenary with the whole class after the group activities are ended to consolidate and extend the children's learning through questions and discussion.

The following chart shows an example of the way in which an activity from this book can be used to achieve the required organisation of the daily maths lesson for Year 4 children.

Counting sticks (page 40)

Start to the lesson	**5–10 minutes**
As a whole class introduction to the lesson, use a counting stick to count forwards and backwards from zero, in tens, twos and fives. Demonstrate the relationships between the multiples; that the right-hand side of the stick shows the tenth multiple and half-way is the fifth multiple, which is half of the tenth multiple (for counting in fives, 25 is half of 50). Encourage the children to look for other relationships involving doubles and halving (for example, the third and sixth multiple) and to describe patterns they notice (if 5 x 5 is 25, 7 x 5 will be 10 more). Use the terms *multiple* and *exactly divisible by*. When describing multiples, ensure the children realise that they go beyond the tenth multiple (for example, 120 is the 12th multiple of ten).	

Main teaching and pupil activities	**about 40 minutes**
Write several small two-digit numbers on the board, for example, 15, 20, 12, 21, 28, 30, and ask the children questions such as: *"Is this number a multiple of two? Is this number exactly divisible by ten?"* Discuss ways of recognising multiples of 2, 3, 4, 5 and 10, for example, all even numbers are exactly divisible by two and all numbers ending in zero are divisible by ten. One group of children could list the multiples of 2, 3, 4, 5 and 10 beyond the tenth multiple. Another group could explore which numbers between 1 and 30 are not divisible by either 2, 3, 4, 5 or 10. The other children, with minimal intervention, could work from **Counting sticks** (page 40, **Developing Numeracy: Numbers and the Number System Year 4**).	

Plenary	**about 10 minutes**
Discuss the numbers the children have found that are exactly divisible by two or more numbers. Show that numbers divisible by two or four are all multiples of four and those divisible by five and ten are all multiples of ten. Remind the children of the importance of knowing by heart the multiplication facts for the 2, 3, 4, 5 and 10 times tables. Revise the multiples using a counting stick.	

Further activities

The following activities provide some practical ideas for whole class mental and oral work. These are intended to introduce or reinforce the main teaching part of the lesson.

Place value, ordering and rounding

Totals
Draw a 'dartboard' as shown here. Ask the children to imagine they have three darts, then set them challenges such as: *"Can you score 13… 83… 310… 405? How many different scores between 100 and 200/between 200 and 300 can you make? What is the highest/lowest score you can make? Can you make a number over 1000?"*

Properties of numbers and number sequences

Counting stick
Hold the stick (which could be a metre stick with every 10 cm coloured) so that all the children can see it. Decide on a number (for example, four) and ask the children to count in fours as you point to each coloured section in turn. When counting back, extend beyond zero. This provides practice in counting on and back and helps the children to remember the multiples of a given number.

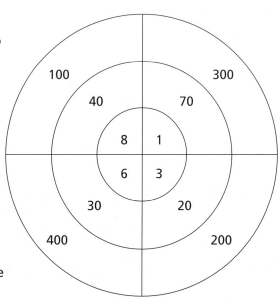

Adding ones and tens

Using a large 100-square, place a piece of plasticine or Blu-Tack on the number 1. Ask a child to pick one o two cards you are holding which show '+1' or '+10'. The child then places a new piece of plasticine on the corresponding number, i.e. 2 or 11. Continue the activity, creating a trail through the 100-square, until no more movement is possible.

Jumping along

Ask the children to count on or back from a given starting number, for example, backwards in threes from 15 to −9 or forwards in 25s from zero. This game can be played in small groups or around the whole class.

Fractions and decimals

Fraction cards

Give the children a selection of fraction cards labelled $\frac{1}{4}$, $\frac{1}{2}$, $1\frac{1}{2}$ etc. Ask the children to arrange themselves in order starting with the smallest fraction.

Decimal darts

Draw a simple 'dartboard' showing a range of decimals with one decimal place, for example: 0.2, 0.4, 0.5 Invite children to choose two numbers and add them together. Ask each child to explain their answers in words.

Selected answers

p 23
1. <   2. <   3. =
4. <   5. >   6. <
7. <
8. <
9. =
10. <
11. =
12. >

p 26
1. between 70 and 75
2. between 100 and 105
3. about 30
4. about 50
5. about 50
6. about 26
7. about 230
8. about 105

p 32
1. −8 °C, −5 °C, −4 °C, −2 °C, 0 °C, 1 °C, 3 °C, 6 °C
2. −9 °C, −3 °C, −1 °C, 0 °C, 2 °C, 3 °C, 4 °C, 5 °C
3. −6 °C, −3 °C, −1 °C, 0 °C, 6 °C, 8 °C, 9 °C, 12 °C
4. −5 °C, −2 °C, −1 °C, 0 °C, 1 °C, 4 °C, 5 °C, 7 °C
5. −9 °C, −6 °C, −4 °C, −2 °C, −1 °C, 2 °C, 5 °C, 8 °C

p 33
Counting back in fives
182, 177, 172, 167, 162, 157, 152, 147, 142, 137, 132, 127, 122, 117, 112, 107, 102, 97, 92, 87, 82, 77, 72, 67, 62, 57, 52, 47, 42, 37, 32, 27, 22, 17, 12, 7, 2, −3

145, 140, 135, 130, 125, 120, 115, 110, 105, 100, 95, 90, 85, 80, 75, 70, 65, 60, 55, 50, 45, 40, 35, 30, 25, 20, 15, 10, 5, 0

101, 96, 91, 86, 81, 76, 71,66, 61, 56, 51, 46, 41, 36, 31, 26, 21, 16, 11, 6, 1, −4

119, 114, 109, 104, 99, 94, 89, 84, 79, 74, 69, 64, 59, 54, 49, 44, 39, 34, 29, 24, 19, 14, 9, 4, −1

158, 153, 148, 143, 138, 133, 128, 123, 118, 113, 108, 103, 98, 93, 88, 83, 78, 73, 68, 63, 58, 53, 48, 43, 38, 33, 28, 23, 18, 13, 8, 3, −2

Counting back in threes
20, 17, 14, 11, 8, 5, 2, −1, −4, −7, −10, −13, −16, −19, −22, −25, −28, −31

30, 27, 24, 21, 18, 15, 12, 9, 6, 3, 0, −3, −6, −9, −12, −15, −18, −21, −24, −27, −30

2, −1, −4, −7, −10, −13, −16, −19, −22, −25, −28, −31

−2, −5, −8, −11, −14, −17, −20, −23, −26, −29, −32

11, 8, 5, 2, −1, −4, −7, −10, −13, −16, −19, −22, −25, −28, −31

Counting back in fours
13, 9, 5, 1, −3, −7, −11, −15, −19, −23, −27, −31, −35, −39, −43

40, 36, 32, 28, 24, 20, 16, 12, 8, 4, 0, −4, −8, −12, −16, −20, −24, −28, −32, −36, −40

−1, −5, −9, −13, −17, −21, −25, −29, −33, −37, −41

10, 6, 2, −2, −6, −10, −14, −18, −22, −26, −30, −34, −38, −42

2, −2, −6, −10, −14, −18, −22, −26, −30, −34, −38, −42

p 36
1. 11, 22, 33, 44, 55, 66, 77, 88
2. 576, 565, 554, 543, 532, 521, 510, 499, 488, 477, 466
3. −77, −66, −55, −44, −33, −22, −11, 0, 11, 22, 33, 44
4. 21, 10, −1, −12, −23, −34, −45, −56, −67, −78, −89, −100
5. −56, −45, −34, −23, −12, −1, 10, 21, 32, 43,
6. 1816, 1827, 1838, 1849, 1860, 1871, 1882, 1893, 1904, 1915

p 39
1. false   2. true
3. true   4. false
5. false   6. true
7. true

p 42
1. $\frac{3}{5}$ 2. $\frac{4}{9}$
3. $\frac{7}{15}$ 4. $\frac{15}{25}$ or $\frac{3}{5}$

p 43
cups of juice: $4\frac{1}{2}$
length in centimetres: $3\frac{3}{4}$
height in metres: $1\frac{1}{4}$
packs of pencils: $3\frac{3}{10}$
pizzas: $2\frac{1}{6}$
bunches of flowers: $4\frac{1}{3}$
bags of sweets: $2\frac{7}{12}$
bars of chocolate: $4\frac{3}{8}$

p 47
1. $\frac{1}{8}$, $\frac{1}{4}$, $\frac{3}{8}$, $\frac{1}{2}$, $\frac{5}{8}$, $\frac{3}{4}$, $\frac{7}{8}$
2. $\frac{1}{10}$, $\frac{1}{5}$, $\frac{3}{10}$, $\frac{2}{5}$, $\frac{1}{2}$, $\frac{3}{5}$, $\frac{7}{10}$, $\frac{4}{5}$

Now try this!
Less than ½: $\frac{3}{10}$, $\frac{1}{7}$, $\frac{1}{3}$, $\frac{1}{9}$, $\frac{2}{10}$, $\frac{1}{10}$, $\frac{2}{6}$, $\frac{1}{5}$, $\frac{4}{10}$, $\frac{1}{4}$;
Greater than ½: $\frac{3}{4}$, $\frac{7}{8}$, $\frac{4}{7}$, $\frac{4}{5}$, $\frac{5}{9}$, $\frac{7}{10}$

p 50
1. 6 m, 3 m, 4 m
2. 5 kg, 2 kg, 1 kg

3. 150 ml, 30 ml, 100 ml
4. 10 m, 4 m, 2 m
5. 25 kg, 10 kg, 5 kg
6. 500 ml, 250 ml, 200 ml

Now try this!
Nahima: £6,
David: £8,
Hardip: £12,
Claire: £4,
£18 is left over

p 53
1. 1 bag of crisps and 1 packet of biscuits
2. 2 apples and 1 packet of biscuits
3. 2 bags of crisps and 3 apples
4. 2 packets of biscuits and 1 bag of crisps
5. 1 apple and 2 packets of biscuits
6. 2 bags of crisps, 1 apple and 1 packet of biscuits
7. 2 packets of biscuits, 3 bags of crisps and 3 apples

p 56
2. 1.3
3. 0.7
4. 1.2
5. 1.7
6. 2.4

7. 1.7   8. 1.5
9. 0.7   10. 1.6
11. 1.6   12. 2.9
13. 2.9   14. 2.3

p 62
1. £2.44
2. £5.31
3. £2.77
4. £4.21
5. 4 m
6. 23.28 m

Thousand and 1000

- **Read the numbers.**
- **Write them in figures.**

5162 · Five thousand, one hundred and sixty-two

Nine thousand and ninety-nine

Two thousand, six hundred and eleven

Ten thousand, one hundred and twenty

- **Write these numbers in words.**

4256 _____

7593 _____

3021 _____

- **Write in words <u>and</u> figures all the numbers between** `3000` **and** `4000` **which are** `multiples of 100` .
- **Write in figures eight numbers which are** `multiples of 50` .
- **Ask a friend to write the figures in words.**

Teachers' note Have spellings available against which the children can check their answers. They may find it helpful to use place value cards during this activity.

Developing Numeracy
Numbers and the Number System
Year 4
© A & C Black 2000

Mix and match 1

- **Cut out the cards.**
- **Find the matching pairs.**

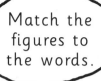
Match the figures to the words.

7 304	Six thousand, two hundred and eighty	6 879
Three thousand, one hundred and thirty-six	4 155	Four thousand, five hundred and fifteen
4 515	Twelve thousand, four hundred and seventeen	Seven thousand, three hundred and four
Four thousand, one hundred and fifty-five	2 012	10 110
12 417	Six thousand, eight hundred and seventy-nine	3 136
Two thousand and twelve	6 280	Ten thousand, one hundred and ten

Now try this!
- **Make five more pairs of matching cards, using any numbers between** $\boxed{100}$ **and** $\boxed{10\,000}$ **.**
- **Mix them up for a friend to match.**

Teachers' note Use the cards on page 9 with this sheet. The sheets could be photocopied onto A3 paper or card. The children can play the game in a group as 'snap' or individually as a memory game of 'pairs'.

Developing Numeracy
Numbers and the Number System
Year 4
© A & C Black 2000

Mix and match 2

Eleven thousand, two hundred and eleven	9 040	Nine thousand and forty
3 704	Eight thousand, six hundred and forty-nine	4 005
Six thousand, four hundred and eighty-nine	2 806	Three thousand and seventeen
10 809	Two thousand, eight hundred and six	Four thousand, six hundred and fifty
Ten thousand, eight hundred and nine	4 650	12 115
8 649	Three thousand, seven hundred and four	6 489
Four thousand and five	3 017	Twelve thousand, one hundred and fifteen
5 382	11 211	Five thousand, three hundred and eighty-two

Developing Numeracy
Numbers and the Number System
Year 4
© A & C Black 2000

What's it worth?

- **Read the digit that is underlined.**
- **Write the value of the digit in figures, then words.**

1.  7 8̲91   800   eight hundred

2.  8 07̲7

3.  5̲ 108

4.  6 346̲

5.  9 2̲11

6.  11̲ 553

7.  1̲2 017

8.  3 413̲

- **Write six different numbers using all of these digits:**

  [4]   [5]   [1]   [0]

- **What is the value of the digit** [5] **in each number?**

Teachers' note Place value cards are useful for supporting children in their understanding of this activity.

Developing Numeracy
Numbers and the Number System
Year 4
© A & C Black 2000

Tropical fish

• **Use the key to colour the fish.**

blue	numbers with 2 in the thousands column
red	numbers with 4 in the hundreds column
yellow	numbers with 6 in the tens column
green	numbers with 8 in the units column

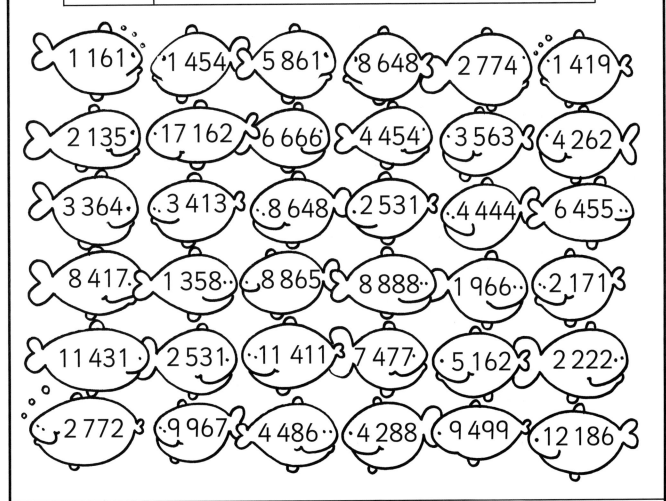

• **Write as many numbers over 1000 as you can, using some, or all, of these digits:**

    1   3   5   7

• **What is the largest number you can make?**

• **What is the smallest number?**

Teachers' note Ask the children to watch out for the five-digit numbers; they may find it easier to read the units column first.

Developing Numeracy
Numbers and the Number System
Year 4
© A & C Black 2000

Brick wall challenge

- Find pairs of bricks that show the same amount.
- Shade them in the same colour or pattern.

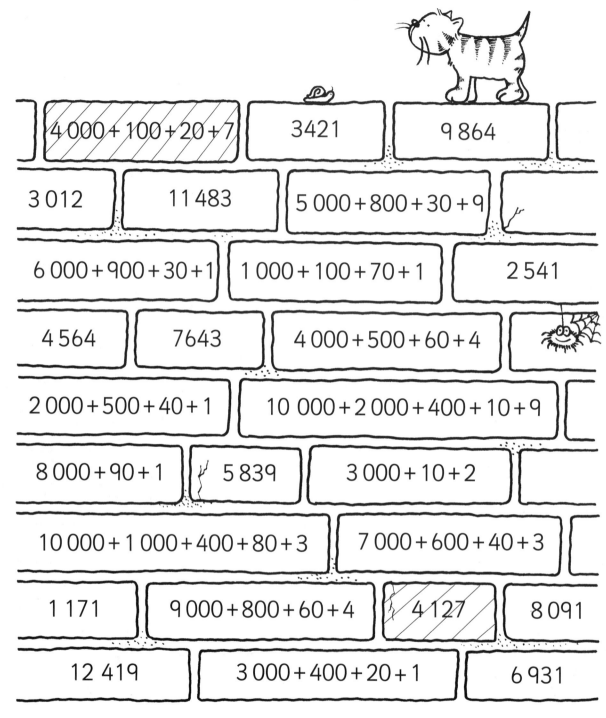

4 000 + 100 + 20 + 7	3421	9 864
3 012	11 483	5 000 + 800 + 30 + 9
6 000 + 900 + 30 + 1	1 000 + 100 + 70 + 1	2 541
4 564	7 643	4 000 + 500 + 60 + 4
2 000 + 500 + 40 + 1	10 000 + 2 000 + 400 + 10 + 9	
8 000 + 90 + 1	5 839	3 000 + 10 + 2
10 000 + 1 000 + 400 + 80 + 3	7 000 + 600 + 40 + 3	
1 171	9 000 + 800 + 60 + 4	4 127	8 091
12 419	3 000 + 400 + 20 + 1	6 931

Now try this!

- Write ten numbers larger than 1000.
- Break down the numbers into thousands, hundreds, tens and units.

Teachers' note Provide place value cards to help the children to complete this activity.

Developing Numeracy
Numbers and the Number System
Year 4
© A & C Black 2000

Addition ladders

- Continue the number sequence up each ladder.
- Follow the instructions on the paint pots.

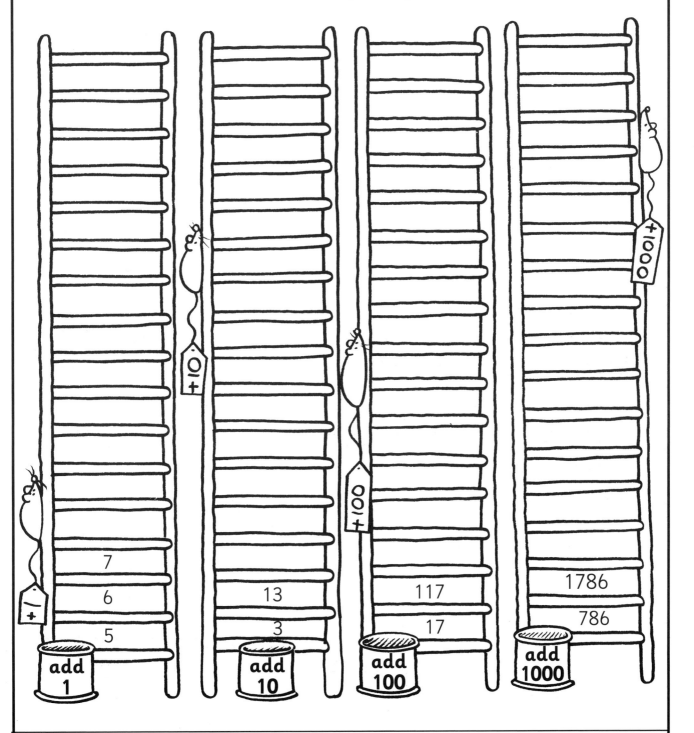

Ladder 1 (add 1): 5, 6, 7

Ladder 2 (add 10): 3, 13 (+10)

Ladder 3 (add 100): 17, 117 (+100)

Ladder 4 (add 1000): 786, 1786 (+1000)

add 1

add 10

add 100

add 1000

Now try this!

- Look closely at each ladder.
- Can you see any patterns?
- Write a rule for each ladder.

Teachers' note The children could discuss the rules they devise in groups. Allow time during the plenary to discuss the rules that the children have devised for each ladder.

Developing Numeracy
Numbers and the Number System
Year 4
© A & C Black 2000

Subtraction snakes

• **Continue the number sequence down each snake.**

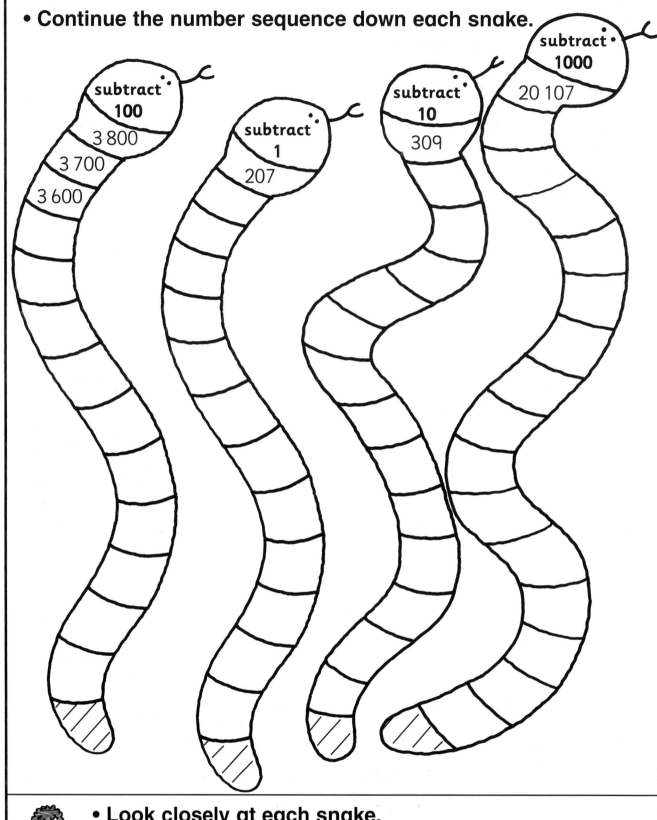

subtract **100**

3 800
3 700
3 600

subtract **1**

207

subtract **10**

309

subtract **1000**

20 107

Now try this!

• **Look closely at each snake.**
• **Can you see any patterns?**
• **Write a rule for each snake.**

Teachers' note As with the addition activity on page 13, the children could discuss the rules they devise in groups. Allow time during the plenary to discuss the rules that the children have devised for each snake.

Developing Numeracy
Numbers and the Number System
Year 4
© A & C Black 2000

Ten more, ten less

- **Follow the number patterns.**
- **Write the missing numbers.**

1.
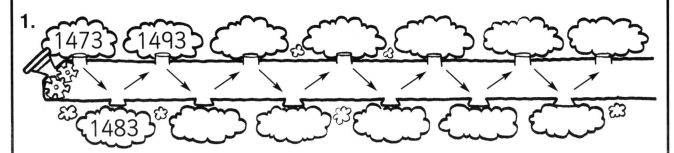

2.
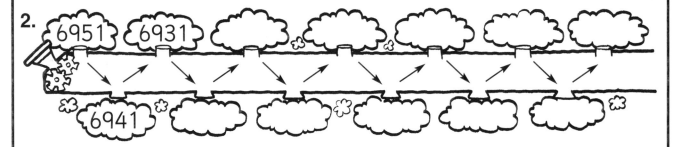

3.
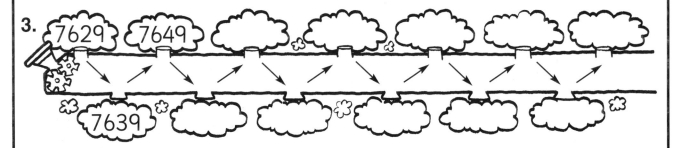

4.
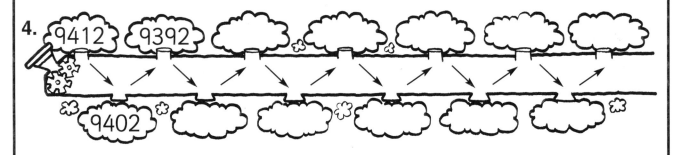

Now try this!

- **Count aloud backwards in tens from $\boxed{9999}$.**
- **How far can you get in three minutes?**

Ask a friend to time you.

Teachers' note Ensure that the children look carefully at each number pattern to decide whether it is going on or back in tens.

Developing Numeracy
Numbers and the Number System
Year 4
© A & C Black 2000

15

Jumping in 100s

- **Find four paths through the grid. Each time, colour a number which is** | 100 more | **or** | 100 less | **than the last number you coloured.**

You can move horizontally, vertically or diagonally…

…and use a different colour for each path.

start			start			start			start		
3451			7893			5372			9407		

3441	3461	3551	7993	7803	7903	5382	5272	9307	9417	9397
3431	3651	3561	3552	7893	7803	5172	5262	9617	9207	9197
3531	3551	3461	7793	7803	7883	5162	5072	9627	9104	9107
3561	3461	3451	7693	7683	7583	5172	5162	9637	9007	9004
3361	3351	3331	7003	7593	5272	5262	5162	8907	8904	9017
3251	3261	3311	7493	7403	5362	5172	8807	8917	8927	8937
3161	3151	7203	7303	7393	7383	5011	5072	8907	9927	9937
3061	3161	3051	6173	7283	7293	4972	6072	9907	9007	9917
3152	2951	3052	6193	7193	8293	5972	4872	9107	9201	8917
3051	2961	2962	7093	8193	9293	6972	4772	9507	9007	8817
2951	3961	6993	8093	9193	293	772	4672	8907	8717	9117
3951	2851	6913	6893	8193	8913	4172	4572	8617	8807	9217

Teachers' note Children who find this activity difficult could write down the numbers needed to help them cross the grid, and then match them to those on the grid to find the path.

Developing Numeracy
Numbers and the Number System
Year 4
© A & C Black 2000

- **Find the pattern for each number sequence.**
- **Continue the sequence.**

Look carefully. Is the pattern addition or subtraction?

1743, 2743, 3743, _____, _____, _____, _____

9871, 8871, 7871, _____, _____, _____, _____

5617, 6617, 7617, _____, _____, _____, _____

13865, 12865, 11865, _____, _____, _____, _____

4762, 5762, 6762, _____, _____, _____, _____

12316, 11316, 10316, _____, _____, _____, _____

9160, 10160, 11160, _____, _____, _____, _____

11784, 10784, 9784, _____, _____, _____, _____

7431, 8431, 9431, _____, _____, _____, _____

16064, 15064, 14064, _____, _____, _____, _____

5172, 6172, 7172, _____, _____, _____, _____

13748, 12748, 11748, _____, _____, _____, _____

1655, 2655, 3655, _____, _____, _____, _____

- **Count on in** 1000s **from 782. Can you reach 20782?**
- **Now count back in** 1000s **from 19999.**

Teachers' note Encourage the children to read each number pattern aloud after completing the activity to check their answers.

Developing Numeracy
Numbers and the Number System
Year 4
© A & C Black 2000

17

Multiplication match

- **Cut out the cards.**
- **Match each multiplication question to the correct answer.**
- **Write a rule for** $\boxed{\text{multiplying by ten}}$.

27 x 10	890	75 x 10	12 x 10	960	370
660	230	440	55 x 10	30 x 10	610
34 x 10	53 x 10	18 x 10	100 x 10	270	480
89 x 10	290	37 x 10	750	83 x 10	740
48 x 10	830	23 x 10	96 x 10	44 x 10	180
61 x 10	74 x 10	530	190	66 x 10	120
19 x 10	1000	300	340	29 x 10	550

Teachers' note The cards can be used to play a game of 'snap'. Ensure that the children write down a rule for multiplying by ten and discuss this during the plenary. Avoid saying 'add a nought' as this leads to misconceptions. Instead, demonstrate the moving of digits across columns.

**Developing Numeracy
Numbers and the Number System
Year 4
© A & C Black 2000**

Division match

- **Find an answer to match each question.**
- **Shade each pair in the same colour or pattern.**
- **Write a rule for** | dividing by ten |.

answers	questions	answers
27	910 ÷ 10	79
58	480 ÷ 10	11
84	870 ÷ 10	74
24	650 ÷ 10	35
41	410 ÷ 10	91
52	150 ÷ 10	15
97	390 ÷ 10	87
60	600 ÷ 10	65
48	840 ÷ 10	39
	970 ÷ 10	
	740 ÷ 10	
	270 ÷ 10	
	350 ÷ 10	
	790 ÷ 10	
	580 ÷ 10	
	240 ÷ 10	
	520 ÷ 10	
	110 ÷ 10	

- **Practise your rule by dividing other** | multiples of ten | **by ten.**
- **Does your rule work?**

Teachers' note Discuss the children's rules as a whole class. It might be appropriate to mention that for numbers that are not multiples of ten (for example, 74) dividing by ten does not involve removing the last digit. Show the movement of digits across columns.

Developing Numeracy
Numbers and the Number System
Year 4
© A & C Black 2000

Mystery numbers

- **Some of the digits in Chloe's maths book have gone missing.**
- **Can you fill them in?**

1. $23 \times 10 = 2\boxed{3}0$

2. $1\square \times 10 = 170$

3. $\square5 \times 10 = 450$

4. $49 \times 10 = \square90$

5. $\square2 \times 10 = 720$

6. $3\square0 \div 10 = 37$

7. $\square50 \div 10 = 95$

8. $680 \div 10 = 6\square$

9. $\square40 \div 10 = 54$

10. $380 \div \square = 38$

11. $7\square \times 10 = \square40$

12. $\square \times 10 = 680$

13. $1\square \times 10 = \square40$

14. $\square9 \times 10 = 2\square0$

15. $\square4 \times 10 = 4\square0$

16. $\square10 \div 10 = 7\square$

17. $5\square0 \div 10 = \square4$

18. $\square80 \div 10 = 2\square$

19. $6\square0 \div 10 = \square3$

20. $170 \div 10 = \square$

21. $550 \div \square = 55$

22. $\square \div 10 = 24$

23. $\square \div 10 = 30$

24. $8000 \div 10 = \square$

Now try this!

- **Choose six numbers between $\boxed{200}$ and $\boxed{400}$.**
- **Multiply each number by ten.**

Example: $235 \times 10 = 2350$

Teachers' note Show the children that multiplying or dividing by ten involves digits moving to the left or right across columns. In the extension activity, encourage the children to read their answers aloud to a partner.

Developing Numeracy
Numbers and the Number System
Year 4
© A & C Black 2000

Snake game

- Take turns to roll a dice and move your counter.
- Multiply the number you land on by 100 .
- Write down the answer and say it aloud.
- Check each other's answers.
- The winner is the first to reach the finish.

Remember, each digit moves two places to the left.

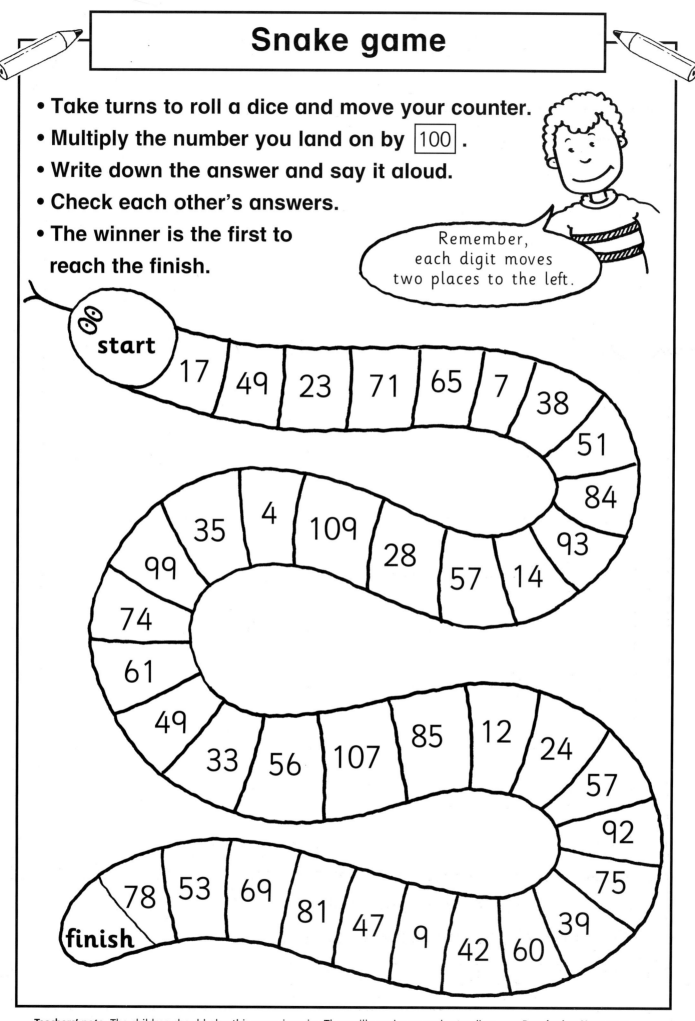

Teachers' note The children should play this game in pairs. They will require an understanding of place value in order to mentally multiply by 100 and say the answer aloud. Ensure that the children say the complete number, for example, 'four thousand seven hundred' and not '47 zero zero'. As an extension activity, they could play the game again, multiplying by 1000.

Developing Numeracy
Numbers and the Number System
Year 4
© A & C Black 2000

Crocodile maths

• **Write a number to make a correct statement.**

The sign is like a crocodile's mouth eating the larger number!

142 ⟩🐊 124

> greater than

1. <u>300</u> is greater than 270 so <u>300</u> > 270

2. ___ is greater than 651 so ___ > 651

3. ___ > 351   4. ___ > 624   5. ___ > 888

6. ___ > 795   7. ___ > 910   8. ___ > 999

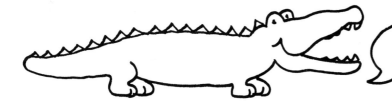

Remember, the crocodile <u>always</u> eats the larger number.

< less than

9. <u>388</u> is less than 412 so <u>388</u> < 412

10. ___ is less than 975 so ___ < 975

11. ___ < 628   12. ___ < 189   13. ___ < 541

14. ___ < 167   15. ___ < 74   16. ___ < 0

= equals

17. <u>417</u> equals 400 + 10 + 7 so <u>417</u> = <u>400 + 10 + 7</u>

18. ___ equals 700 + 6 so ___ = ___

19. ___ equals 800 + 40 + 5 so ___ = ___

20. ___ equals 300 + 90 + 3 so ___ = ___

Now try this!

• **Make up ten more sentences using these words:**

| greater than | less than | equals |

Teachers' note Explain to the children that the wider end of the greater than/less than symbol is always next to the larger number.

Developing Numeracy
Numbers and the Number System
Year 4
© A & C Black 2000

More, less or the same?

- **Write a symbol to make a correct statement.**

| > | < | = |

The < and > signs are like a crocodile's mouth eating the larger number!

142 > 124   124 < 142

1. 562 ☐ 643   **2.** 414 ☐ 441   **3.** 62 ☐ 62

4. 479 ☐ 497   **5.** 862 ☐ 628   **6.** 97 ☐ 197

7. two hundred and seventy-four ☐ 376

8. one thousand and fifty-five ☐ 1202

9. eight hundred and eight ☐ 808

10. six hundred and twelve ☐ 621

11. two thousand four hundred ☐ 2400

12. six thousand and seven ☐ 607

- **How many different statements can you make using some, or all, of these numbers and symbols?**

| 3 | 5 | 5 | 2 | > | < | = |

Examples: 3 < 52   355 > 2   5 = 5

Teachers' note Remind the children that the wider end of the greater than/less than symbol is always next to the larger number.

Developing Numeracy
Numbers and the Number System
Year 4
© A & C Black 2000

Stuck in the middle

• **Write any number that comes between the numbers on either side.**

1. 4562 _5555_ 7241
2. 3174 _____ 5726
3. 6286 _____ 7175
4. 9814 _____ 9673
5. 8495 _____ 7991
6. 4756 _____ 3412

7. 9357 _____ 8941
8. 2913 _____ 3709
9. 4603 _____ 5127
10. 7159 _____ 8004
11. 3864 _____ 3519
12. 5981 _____ 6273

• **Write two numbers that come between the numbers on either side.**

13. 9421 _9163_ _8110_ 7019
14. 6387 _____ _____ 8535
15. 1394 _____ _____ 581
16. 5062 _____ _____ 6537
17. 8933 _____ _____ 9999

Write the numbers in order.

• **Write eight more number sequences. Leave gaps for a friend to fill in.**

Developing Numeracy
Numbers and the Number System
Year 4
© A & C Black 2000

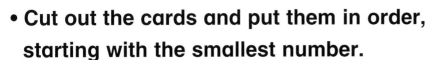

Think of a number

- Cut out the cards and put them in order, starting with the smallest number.
- Choose any two cards and write down the numbers.
- Write another number that lies between them.
- Do the same for five more pairs of cards.

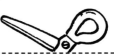

1917	4278	1784
5793	4104	8175
4953	4563	5817
7536	4912	1428

Teachers' note This activity can be played as a game in pairs. The children place the cards face down. They take turns to pick two cards and give a number that lies between the numbers on the cards.

Developing Numeracy
Numbers and the Number System
Year 4
© A & C Black 2000

Where is it roughly?

- **Estimate which numbers the arrows are pointing to.**

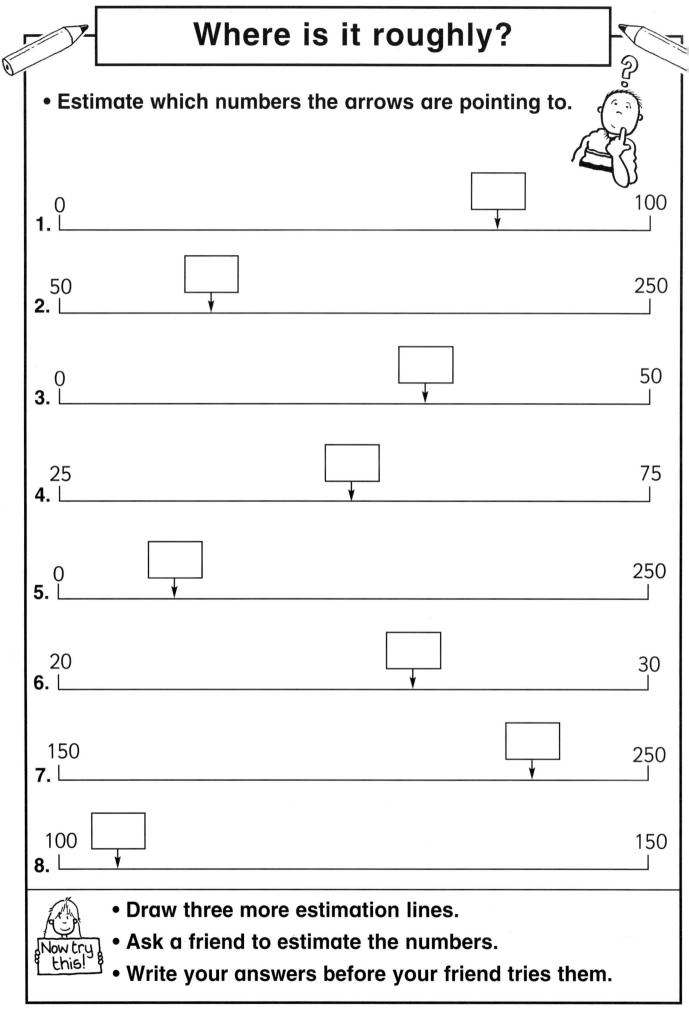

1. 0   100

2. 50   250

3. 0   50

4. 25   75

5. 0   250

6. 20   30

7. 150   250

8. 100   150

Now try this!

- **Draw three more estimation lines.**
- **Ask a friend to estimate the numbers.**
- **Write your answers before your friend tries them.**

Teachers' note Practise estimating numbers on a line with the whole class. Discuss dividing up the line into equal parts to help identify the numbers. Revise the language of estimation with the children.

Developing Numeracy
Numbers and the Number System
Year 4
© A & C Black 2000

The maths menace strikes

The maths menace has been scoffing sweets!
The label tells you how many sweets
were in the jar when it was full.

Don't count
the sweets.

• **Estimate how many sweets are left.**

There are
about

```
┌──────────┐
│          │
└──────────┘
```
sweets.

100

There are
about

```
┌──────────┐
│          │
└──────────┘
```
sweets.

50

There are
about

```
┌──────────┐
│          │
└──────────┘
```
sweets.

150

There are
about

```
┌──────────┐
│          │
└──────────┘
```
sweets.

150

There are

```
┌──────────┐
│          │
└──────────┘
```
sweets.

250

There are
about

```
┌──────────┐
│          │
└──────────┘
```
sweets.

150

Now try this!

• **Write down how you worked out each answer.**
• **Discuss it with a friend. Did you both work
  out your answers in the same way?**

Teachers' note During the plenary session, discuss how the children made their estimates.

**Developing Numeracy
Numbers and the Number System
Year 4
© A & C Black 2000**

27

Buzzing bees

These statements tell you about rounding to the nearest ten.

613 rounded to the nearest ten is 610.

435 rounded to the nearest ten is 440.

827 rounded to the nearest ten is 830.

- **Round the number on each bee to the nearest ten.**
- **Join the bee to the correct flower.**

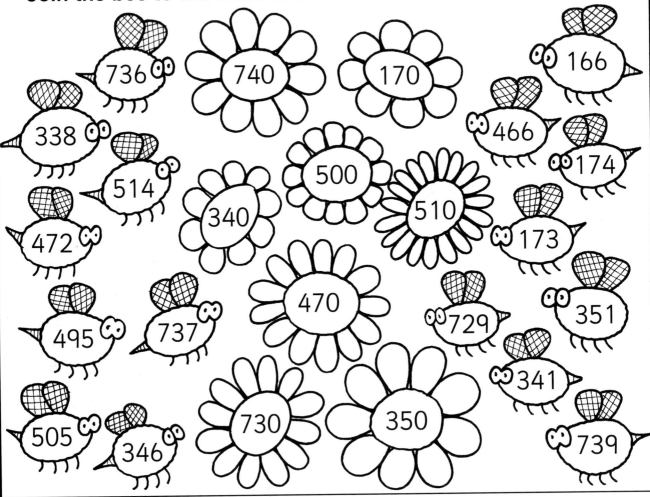

- ● **Pick three cards from a pack of playing cards.**
- ● **Use the numbers on the cards to make a three-digit number.**
- ● **Round this number to the nearest ten.**
- ● **Do this five times. Use different cards each time.**

Teachers' note Suggest that the children use a different colour for each flower and matching bees. For the extension, you could remove the picture cards and the tens. Alternatively, you could leave in the picture cards and the tens and allow the children to choose how they use them, for example, a picture card could be used as a 'wild' card.

Developing Numeracy
Numbers and the Number System
Year 4
© A & C Black 2000

Round and round

These statements tell you about rounding to the nearest 100.

> 233 rounded to the nearest hundred is 200.

> 456 rounded to the nearest hundred is 500.

- **Round the numbers in the balloons to the nearest 100.**
- **Write the number.**

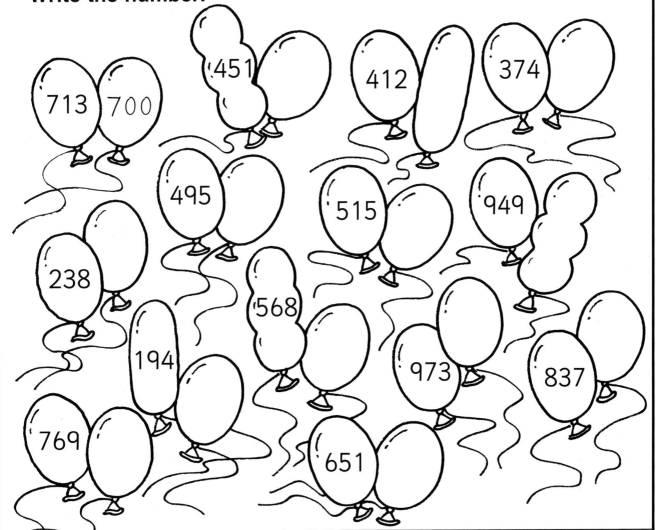

- **Pick four cards from a pack of playing cards.**
- **Use the numbers on the cards to make a four-digit number.**
- **Round this number to the nearest 100.**
- **Do this five times. Use different cards each time.**

Teachers' note Remind the children that when a number is rounded to the nearest 100, the answer will always be a multiple of 100. For the extension, you could remove the picture cards and the tens. Alternatively, you could leave in the picture cards and the tens and allow the children to choose how they use them, for example, a picture card could be used as a 'wild' card.

Developing Numeracy
Numbers and the Number System
Year 4
© A & C Black 2000

Roadhog

Here are the distances that two lorries travel each day.

- **Round these distances to the** nearest 10 miles .

Monday	353 miles	350 miles
Tuesday	176 miles	
Wednesday	38 miles	
Thursday	214 miles	
Friday	419 miles	
Saturday	99 miles	

- **Round these distances to the** nearest 100 miles .

Monday	220 miles	
Tuesday	684 miles	
Wednesday	178 miles	
Thursday	314 miles	
Friday	454 miles	
Saturday	50 miles	

Now try this!

- **Find a distance table in an atlas or road map.**
- **Choose six distances and round them to the**
  nearest 10 miles   nearest 100 miles

Teachers' note Remind the children that when they round to the nearest 10, the answer will be a multiple of 10, and when they round to the nearest 100, the answer will be a multiple of 100.

Developing Numeracy
Numbers and the Number System
Year 4
© A & C Black 2000

Negative numbers

• **Write the missing numbers.**

Look carefully. Some are negative numbers.

–5 –4 ☐ –2 –1 0 1 ☐ 3 4 5

–8 –7 –6 ☐ –4 –3 ☐ –1 0 1 2

–1 –1 ☐ –8 –7 –6 –5 ☐ –3 –2 –1

–3 –2 ☐ 0 1 2 ☐ 4 5 6 7

–5 –4 –3 ☐ –1 0 ☐ 2 3 4 5

–6 ☐ –4 ☐ –2 –1 0 1 2 3 4

• **Write the temperature shown on each thermometer.**

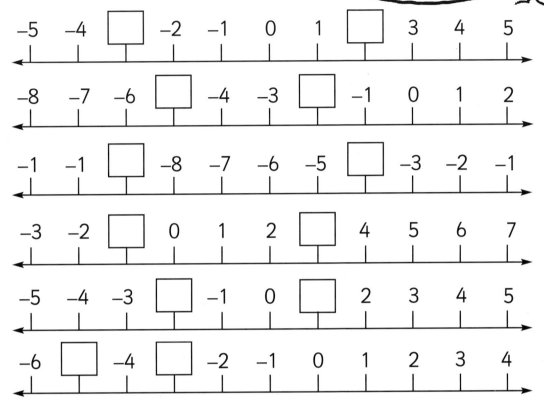

| ☐ °C | ☐ °C | ☐ °C | ☐ °C | ☐ °C | ☐ °C |

Teachers' note Make sure that the children have plenty of practice in saying aloud numbers backwards beyond zero.

Developing Numeracy
Numbers and the Number System
Year 4
© A & C Black 2000

31

• **Put these temperatures in order, starting with the coolest.**

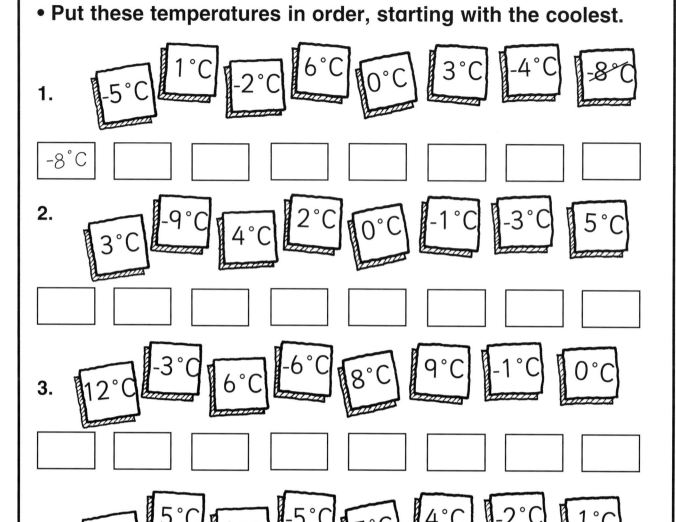

1. -5°C 1°C -2°C 6°C 0°C 3°C -4°C ~~-8°C~~

-8°C							

2. 3°C -9°C 4°C 2°C 0°C -1°C -3°C 5°C

3. 12°C -3°C 6°C -6°C 8°C 9°C -1°C 0°C

4. -1°C 5°C 0°C -5°C 7°C 4°C -2°C 1°C

5. -1°C 2°C -2°C -4°C 5°C -6°C -9°C 8°C

Now try this!

• **Make eight temperature cards of your own.**
• **Mix them up, then see how quickly you can order them from** coolest to warmest .

Teachers' note During the whole class mental/oral work, construct a number line from –10 to 10 and discuss and compare the positions of numbers on the line.

Developing Numeracy
Numbers and the Number System
Year 4
© A & C Black 2000

Number nests

- **Count back from each number in** [fives].
  Stop when you reach or pass [zero].

Write down the numbers.

145 119 158 182 101

- **Count back from each number in** [threes]. **Stop when you reach or pass** [–30].

30 –2 11 20 2

- **Count back from each number in** [fours]. **Stop when you reach or pass** [–40].

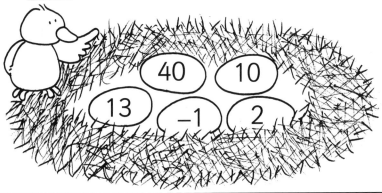

40 10 13 –1 2

Now try this!

- **Play a counting game with a friend.**
- **Choose a number. Ask your friend to count on or back in** [threes].
- **How far can your friend count?**

Try counting in fours, fives and sixes, too!

Teachers' note Children need plenty of practice in counting forwards and backwards past zero. Use a number line to demonstrate number jumps of different sizes. The children should write down their answers in the main activity. Some children may need a number line to check their friends' counting in the extension activity.

Developing Numeracy
Numbers and the Number System
Year 4
© A & C Black 2000

33

River trail

- **Count from** $\boxed{0}$ **in steps of** $\boxed{25}$.
- **When you reach** $\boxed{400}$ **, count back to** $\boxed{-100}$.
- **Write the numbers on the stepping stones.**

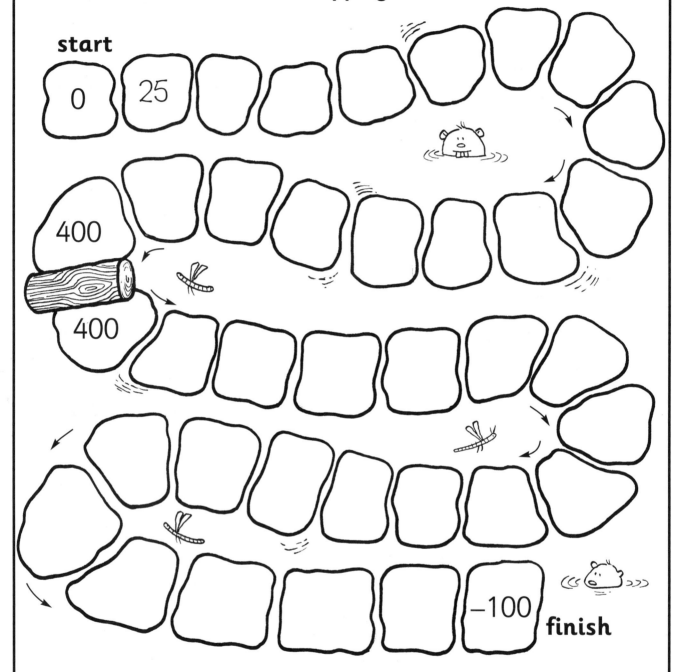

- **Draw your own stepping stones. Count from** $\boxed{2}$ **in steps of** $\boxed{25}$.
- **When you reach** $\boxed{502}$ **, count back to** $\boxed{-102}$.

Teachers' note The children could make paper stepping stones and put them in order on the floor. This sheet could be masked before photocopying for a flexible resource, or you could add numbers before photocopying to help children who need extra support.

34

**Developing Numeracy
Numbers and the Number System
Year 4**
© A & C Black 2000

Crazy counting

- **Cut out the cards and put them face down.**
- **Take turns to pick a card and follow the instructions.**
- **Ask a friend to check your answers.**

Write down the numbers.

Count on from −60 to 120 in steps of 10 .	Count back from 410 to −70 in steps of 40 .	Count on from −70 to 200 in steps of 30 .
Count back from 370 to −110 in steps of 30 .	Count on from −50 to 250 in steps of 20 .	Count on from −85 to 135 in steps of 20 .
Count on from −310 to 240 in steps of 50 .	Count back from 444 to −156 in steps of 40 .	Count back from 75 to −85 in steps of 10 .
Count back from 227 to −53 in steps of 20 .	Count back from 320 to −280 in steps of 50 .	Count on from −60 to 270 in steps of 30 .
Count back from 245 to −135 in steps of 20 .	Count on from −410 to 240 in steps of 50 .	Count back from 220 to −50 in steps of 30 .
Count back from 280 to −320 in steps of 50 .	Count on from −90 to 390 in steps of 40 .	Count on from −207 to 353 in steps of 40 .

Teachers' note This game can be used as a mental exercise for the whole class, or in spare minutes (for example, wet playtime) for individuals or pairs. Children who find this activity difficult could use an appropriate number line.

Developing Numeracy
Numbers and the Number System
Year 4
© A & C Black 2000

Numbers on the line

- **Continue the number patterns on the washing lines.**

1.

11 22 33

2.
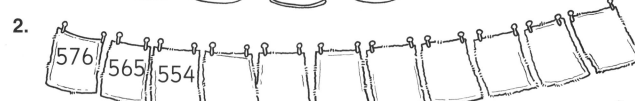
576 565 554

3.

−77 −66 −55

4.

21 10 −1

5.

−56 −45 −34

6.
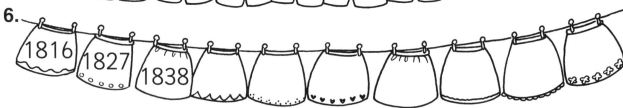
1816 1827 1838

- **Write a rule to explain what happens when you**

| add 11 | | subtract 11 |

- **Write three number patterns that go** | on in nines |
  or | back in nines | **. Start from different numbers.**
- **Write a rule to explain what happens when you**

| add nine | | subtract nine |

Developing Numeracy
Numbers and the Number System
Year 4
© A & C Black 2000

Pattern puzzles

1. Colour the multiples of 9 .

1	2	3	4	5	6	7	8	9	10
11	12	13	14	15	16	17	18	19	20
21	22	23	24	25	26	27	28	29	30
31	32	33	34	35	36	37	38	39	40
41	42	43	44	45	46	47	48	49	50
51	52	53	54	55	56	57	58	59	60
61	62	63	64	65	66	67	68	69	70
71	72	73	74	75	76	77	78	79	80
81	82	83	84	85	86	87	88	89	90
91	92	93	94	95	96	97	98	99	100

2. Colour the multiples of 6 .

1	20	21	40	41	60	61	80	81	100
2	19	22	39	42	59	62	79	82	99
3	18	23	38	43	58	63	78	83	98
4	17	24	37	44	57	64	77	84	97
5	16	25	36	45	56	65	76	85	96
6	15	26	35	46	55	66	75	86	95
7	14	27	34	47	54	67	74	87	94
8	13	28	33	48	53	68	73	88	93
9	12	29	32	49	52	69	72	89	92
10	11	30	31	50	51	70	71	90	91

3. Colour the multiples of 4 .

73	74	75	76	77	78	79	80	81	82
72	43	44	45	46	47	48	49	50	83
71	42	21	22	23	24	25	26	51	84
70	41	20	7	8	9	10	27	52	85
69	40	19	6	1	2	11	28	53	86
68	39	18	5	4	3	12	29	54	87
67	38	17	16	15	14	13	30	55	88
66	37	36	35	34	33	32	31	56	89
65	64	63	62	61	60	59	58	57	90
100	99	98	97	96	95	94	93	92	91

4. Colour the multiples of 2 .

1	3	6	10	15	21	28	36	45	55
2	5	9	14	20	27	35	44	54	64
4	8	13	19	26	34	43	53	63	72
7	12	18	25	33	42	52	62	71	79
11	17	24	32	41	51	61	70	78	85
16	23	31	40	50	60	69	77	84	90
22	30	39	49	59	68	76	83	89	94
29	38	48	58	67	75	82	88	93	97
37	47	57	66	74	81	87	92	96	99
46	56	65	73	80	86	91	95	98	100

- **On grid 2, use a new colour to shade the** multiples of 3 .
- **What do you notice about the** multiples of 6 **?**

Teachers' note This sheet can be copied and different multiple patterns explored. For example, ask the children to colour the multiples of four in all four grids. The grids deliberately present the numbers 1-100 in a variety of arrangements, to focus the children's attention on finding the multiples of each number.

Developing Numeracy
Numbers and the Number System
Year 4
© A & C Black 2000

Odd or even?

- **Colour all the** [even numbers] **blue.**
- **Colour all the** [odd numbers] **yellow.**

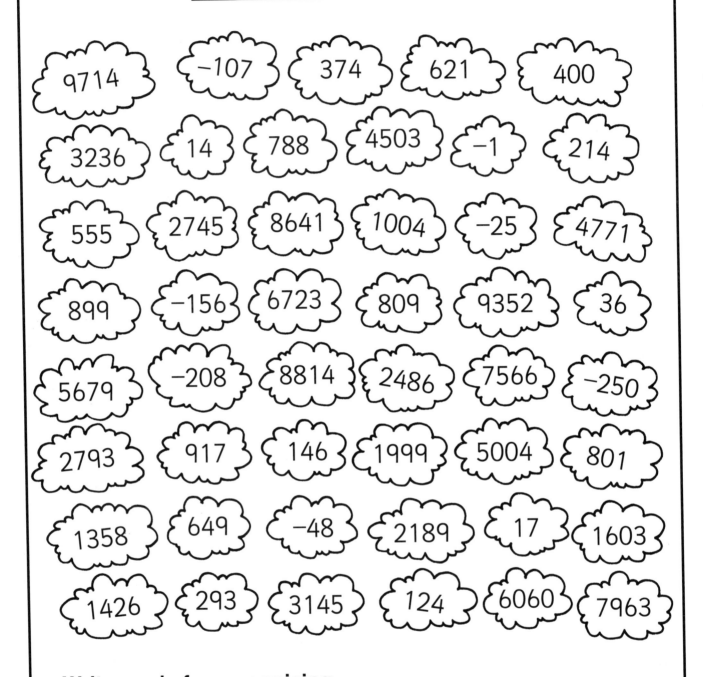

9714   –107   374   621   400

3236   14   788   4503   –1   214

555   2745   8641   1004   –25   4771

899   –156   6723   809   9352   36

5679   –208   8814   2486   7566   –250

2793   917   146   1999   5004   801

1358   649   –48   2189   17   1603

1426   293   3145   124   6060   7963

- **Write a rule for recognising**

  [even numbers]   [odd numbers]

- **Swap your rules with a friend.**
- **Test each other's rules. Do the rules work?**

Teachers' note Ensure that the children have time to discuss each other's rules.

Developing Numeracy
Numbers and the Number System
Year 4
© A & C Black 2000

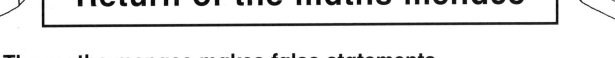

The maths menace makes false statements.

Can you spot his statements?

- Test each statement.

  Is it true or false? or ✗

- Write explanations for your answers.

1.
The last digit of an even number is 0, 2, 4, 6 or 7. ☐

2.
If you add two even numbers together, the answer is always even. ☐

3.
Every even number is followed by an odd number. ☐

4.
The first digit of an odd number is 1, 3, 7, 9 or 5. ☐

5.
If you add two odd numbers together the answer is always odd. ☐

6.
If you add an odd and an even number together the answer is always odd. ☐

7.
If you double a number ending in the digit 0 or 2, the answer will end in the digit 0 or 4. ☐

- **Write a statement about**

  | adding three even numbers |

  | adding two even numbers and an odd number |

- **Test your statements to see whether they are true.**

Teachers' note Make sure the children realise that giving one example is insufficient to prove a general statement, although one example can be enough to disprove it.

Developing Numeracy
Numbers and the Number System
Year 4
© A & C Black 2000

39

Counting sticks

The numbers on this counting stick are exactly divisible by three .

| 3 | 6 | 9 | 12 | 15 | 18 | 21 | 24 | 27 | 30 |

1. Which numbers on the stick are exactly divisible by two **?**

☐ ☐ ☐ ☐ ☐

2. Which numbers on the stick are
exactly divisible by three and two **?**

☐ ☐ ☐ ☐ ☐

3. Write multiples of five **on this counting stick.**

4. Write multiples of four **on this counting stick.**

5. Write a number that is exactly divisible by

four and three ____   five and two ____

four and five ____   three and five ____

• **Write a statement about numbers that are**
exactly divisible by two and four
exactly divisible by five and two

Teachers' note During the whole class session, demonstrate with examples that multiples of a number are also exactly divisible by that number.

Developing Numeracy
Numbers and the Number System
Year 4
© A & C Black 2000

Fairground hoopla

• **Ring the numbers that belong on each hoopla stall.**

multiples of 5

(5)   11   45   51   10
24   35   41   15
   29   31   50

not multiples of 2

   6   5   9   2
11
   8   7   10   13
            4   21
         18
   8   15   16

multiples of 10

10   30   45   60
5   50   75   40
25   70   85   20

multiples of 5 and 10

   18   15   61   10
14   45   100   30   17
41   25   19   70

• **Use the key to draw the correct shapes around the numbers.**

Key

○	numbers divisible by 2
□	numbers divisible by 5
△	numbers divisible by 10

(2)   30   65
         14
            5
         55   15
                  4
95   50   35
         16   8   20   90
40   12   75   70   6
      85
18   60   100   10   45

Teachers' note Remind the children to read the instructions carefully for each part of this sheet.
They could be asked to sort the numbers into a Venn diagram. In the extension activity, the
children should realise that some numbers will have more than one shape around them.

Developing Numeracy
Numbers and the Number System
Year 4
© A & C Black 2000

Parts of a whole

• **Write the correct fraction for each picture.**

1. shaded area = ☐

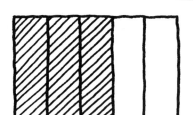

2. spotty socks = ☐

3. white balls = ☐

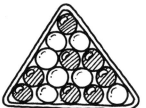

4. black grapes = ☐

• **Colour these pictures to show:**

5.
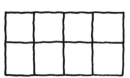
$\dfrac{5}{12}$

6.
$\dfrac{7}{12}$

7.
$\dfrac{7}{8}$

8.
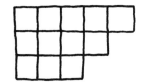
$\dfrac{4}{9}$

9.

$\dfrac{2}{5}$

10.
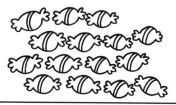
$\dfrac{9}{15}$

• **Draw and colour pictures to show these fractions.**

Now try this!

$\dfrac{7}{9}$ $\dfrac{2}{3}$ $\dfrac{5}{8}$ $\dfrac{4}{5}$ $\dfrac{1}{2}$ $\dfrac{3}{4}$

Teachers' note In the black grapes example, some children may notice that $\frac{15}{25}$ is equivalent to $\frac{3}{5}$. This can be used as a discussion point during the plenary session.

Developing Numeracy
Numbers and the Number System
Year 4
© A & C Black 2000

Picture match

- **Match the fractions to the correct pictures.**
- **Shade each matching pair a different colour.**

cups of juice

$2\frac{7}{12}$

length in centimetres

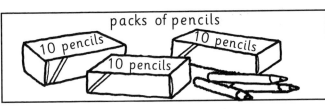

height in metres

$2\frac{1}{6}$

packs of pencils

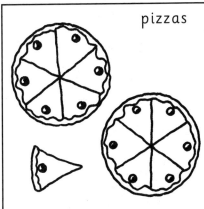

$4\frac{3}{8}$

$1\frac{1}{4}$

pizzas

$3\frac{3}{10}$

bunches of flowers

bags of sweets

$3\frac{3}{4}$

bars of chocolate

$4\frac{1}{2}$

$4\frac{1}{3}$

- **Draw pictures to show these fractions.**

$3\frac{1}{3}$ $5\frac{2}{3}$ $4\frac{1}{4}$ $2\frac{3}{4}$ $1\frac{3}{4}$ $2\frac{2}{3}$ $3\frac{1}{6}$ $4\frac{5}{7}$

Teachers' note It is important to stress the 'unit', for example, $4\frac{1}{3}$ <u>bunches</u> of flowers, as the children may just count the individual objects (13 flowers).

Developing Numeracy
Numbers and the Number System
Year 4
© A & C Black 2000

Fractions in the news

- **Match the fractions to the news stories.**

$\frac{1}{3}$ $1\frac{1}{3}$

$3\frac{1}{4}$ $1\frac{1}{2}$ $2\frac{1}{5}$

$12\frac{1}{2}$

Boy runs three and a quarter miles

One third of a class are ill with chicken pox!

$2\frac{2}{5}$

Champion athlete reaches speed of twelve and a half miles an hour

NAILS FOR SALE: one and six eighths inches long

Mrs Jones waits two and three quarter hours for a taxi

Man eats six and two thirds pizzas!

New record in long jump: ten and three tenths metres

Snail crawls two and two fifths metres in an hour!

$\frac{2}{3}$

$6\frac{2}{3}$ $6\frac{1}{3}$

$3\frac{1}{3}$ $\frac{1}{2}$ $2\frac{3}{4}$

$2\frac{1}{4}$ $10\frac{3}{10}$ $1\frac{6}{8}$

Now try this!

- **Make five cards. Write a fraction on each card.**
- **Make five matching cards with the same fractions written in words.**
- **Mix up the cards and play 'snap' with a friend.**

Teachers' note Ask the children to shade each matching pair a different colour. Point out to them that some fractions will be left over once they have matched the pairs. In the extension activity, the children should play 'snap' by matching a fraction in figures to the same fraction in words.

Developing Numeracy
Numbers and the Number System
Year 4
© A & C Black 2000

Equivalence match

- Cut out the cards.
- Match the | equivalent | fractions.

$\frac{3}{4}$	$\frac{1}{2}$	$\frac{2}{10}$	$\frac{1}{3}$	$\frac{2}{12}$	$\frac{4}{8}$
$\frac{2}{3}$	$\frac{2}{18}$	$\frac{4}{12}$	$\frac{6}{8}$	$\frac{4}{20}$	$\frac{1}{4}$
$\frac{7}{14}$	$\frac{2}{5}$	$\frac{12}{16}$	$\frac{3}{6}$	$\frac{50}{100}$	$\frac{4}{16}$
$\frac{2}{8}$	$\frac{2}{14}$	$\frac{8}{20}$	$\frac{1}{5}$	$\frac{8}{12}$	$\frac{2}{6}$
$\frac{5}{15}$	$\frac{2}{4}$	$\frac{10}{40}$	$\frac{4}{16}$	$\frac{1}{7}$	$\frac{4}{10}$
$\frac{4}{6}$	$\frac{5}{20}$	$\frac{3}{9}$	$\frac{1}{6}$	$\frac{5}{10}$	$\frac{12}{16}$
$\frac{10}{30}$	$\frac{3}{15}$	$\frac{8}{16}$	$\frac{25}{50}$	$\frac{1}{9}$	$\frac{6}{9}$

Teachers' note This page could be photocopied on to A3. Provide fraction walls for the children to use to check equivalences. If children need additional support with this activity, remove some of the more difficult fractions.

Developing Numeracy
Numbers and the Number System
Year 4
© A & C Black 2000

Fraction action game

- **Take turns to roll a dice and move your counter.**
- **When you land on a fraction, work out what fraction you need to add to make one whole.**

  Example: $\frac{1}{2} + \frac{1}{2} = 1$

- **Write down your answers.**

Teachers' note This game can be played by one to four players. Each group will need a dice and a counter for each player. The children can be encouraged to check each other's answers. As an extension activity, ask the children to make their own version of the game, substituting different fractions.

Developing Numeracy
Numbers and the Number System
Year 4
© A & C Black 2000

Ordering fractions

• Write the fractions in order, starting with the smallest.

1.

$$\frac{3}{8} \qquad \frac{1}{4} \qquad \frac{7}{8} \qquad \frac{5}{8} \qquad \frac{1}{2} \qquad \frac{1}{8} \qquad \frac{3}{4}$$

_____

2.

$$\frac{3}{10} \qquad \frac{1}{2} \qquad \frac{4}{5} \qquad \frac{1}{10} \qquad \frac{2}{5} \qquad \frac{7}{10} \qquad \frac{3}{5} \qquad \frac{1}{5}$$

_____

• Write these fractions on the correct boards.

$\frac{3}{4}$	$\frac{3}{10}$	$\frac{7}{8}$	$\frac{1}{7}$	$\frac{4}{7}$	$\frac{1}{3}$	$\frac{1}{9}$	$\frac{2}{10}$
$\frac{4}{5}$	$\frac{1}{10}$	$\frac{2}{6}$	$\frac{5}{9}$	$\frac{1}{5}$	$\frac{4}{10}$	$\frac{7}{10}$	$\frac{1}{4}$

Less than $\frac{1}{2}$

$\frac{3}{10}$

Greater than $\frac{1}{2}$

$\frac{3}{4}$

Teachers' note Encourage the children to find the equivalent fractions to help them to order fractions with different denominators. Some children may need a fraction wall to help them with this activity.

Developing Numeracy
Numbers and the Number System
Year 4
© A & C Black 2000

Dividing with fractions

• Write a fraction to complete these statements.

1. $18 \div 2 = \boxed{\frac{1}{2}}$ of 18

2. $12 \div 3 = \boxed{}$ of 12

3. $15 \div 3 = \boxed{}$ of 15

4. $8 \div 2 = \boxed{}$ of 8

5. $10 \div 5 = \boxed{}$ of 10

6. $20 \div 4 = \boxed{}$ of 20

7. $12 \div 6 = \boxed{}$ of 12

8. $15 \div 5 = \boxed{}$ of 15

9. $14 \div 2 = \boxed{}$ of 14

10. $9 \div 3 = \boxed{}$ of 9

11. $21 \div 7 = \boxed{}$ of 21

12. $16 \div 8 = \boxed{}$ of 16

13. $18 \div 9 = \boxed{}$ of 18

14. $12 \div 4 = \boxed{}$ of 12

15. $25 \div 5 = \boxed{}$ of 25

16. $14 \div 7 = \boxed{}$ of 14

17. $24 \div 8 = \boxed{}$ of 24

18. $36 \div 6 = \boxed{}$ of 36

Now try this!

• **Copy out the statements.**
• **Add another equals sign and write the answer.**

Example: $18 \div 2 = \frac{1}{2}$ of $18 = 9$

Teachers' note You could also give this kind of question to the children orally.

Developing Numeracy
Numbers and the Number System
Year 4
© A & C Black 2000

48

Shrinking numbers

• **Solve these puzzles.**

1. What is one tenth of...

50? [ ]   100? [ ]   30? [ ]   500? [ ]

2. What is one fifth of...

25? [ ]   40? [ ]   15? [ ]   100? [ ]

3. What is one quarter of...

16? [ ]   32? [ ]   40? [ ]   400? [ ]

4. What is $\frac{1}{2}$ of...

20? [ ]   50? [ ]   100? [ ]   12? [ ]

5. What is $\frac{1}{6}$ of...

12? [ ]   60? [ ]   24? [ ]   36? [ ]

6. What is $\frac{1}{8}$ of...

8? [ ]   40? [ ]   16? [ ]   80? [ ]

 • **Write the puzzles as division statements.**

Example: one tenth of 50 = 50 ÷ 10 = 5

Teachers' note Encourage the children to use division to find the answers and multiplication to check them.

Developing Numeracy
Numbers and the Number System
Year 4
© A & C Black 2000

Fractions of measures

• **Complete the missing measurements.**

1.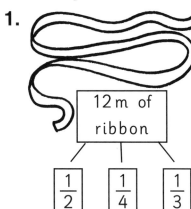

12 m of ribbon

| $\frac{1}{2}$ | $\frac{1}{4}$ | $\frac{1}{3}$ |

6 m   3 m   4 m

2.

10 kg of potatoes

| $\frac{1}{2}$ | $\frac{1}{5}$ | $\frac{1}{10}$ |

3.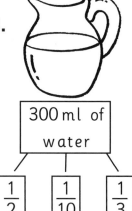

300 ml of water

| $\frac{1}{2}$ | $\frac{1}{10}$ | $\frac{1}{3}$ |

4.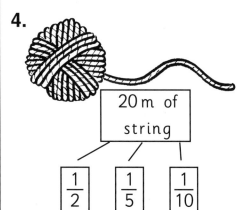

20 m of string

| $\frac{1}{2}$ | $\frac{1}{5}$ | $\frac{1}{10}$ |

5.

50 kg of me!

| $\frac{1}{2}$ | $\frac{1}{5}$ | $\frac{1}{10}$ |

6.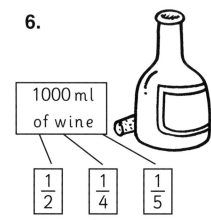

1000 ml of wine

| $\frac{1}{2}$ | $\frac{1}{4}$ | $\frac{1}{5}$ |

• **Give each child the correct fraction of** £48 **.**

Give Nahima $\frac{1}{8}$.  £6

Give David $\frac{1}{6}$.

Give Hardip $\frac{1}{4}$.

Give Claire $\frac{1}{12}$.

• **How much money is left over?**

Teachers' note Encourage the children to write the unit of measurement for each answer.

Developing Numeracy
Numbers and the Number Syste
Year 4
© A & C Black 2000

Money matters

• **Write the answers to these money questions.**

1. $\frac{1}{2}$ of £1 = $\boxed{50p}$ 2. $\frac{1}{4}$ of £2 = $\boxed{}$

3. $\frac{1}{5}$ of 10p = $\boxed{}$ 4. $\frac{1}{6}$ of £3 = $\boxed{}$

5. $\frac{1}{4}$ of 20p = $\boxed{}$ 6. $\frac{1}{10}$ of £30 = $\boxed{}$

7. $\frac{1}{3}$ of 90p = $\boxed{}$ 8. $\frac{1}{5}$ of £50 = $\boxed{}$

• **Ring the purse that contains the smaller amount.**

1.
$\frac{1}{2}$ of 20p $\frac{1}{10}$ of 20p

2.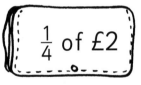
$\frac{1}{5}$ of £1 $\frac{1}{4}$ of £2

3.
$\frac{1}{3}$ of 90p $\frac{1}{2}$ of 40p

4.
$\frac{1}{6}$ of 60p $\frac{1}{5}$ of 40p

5.
$\frac{1}{5}$ of £5 $\frac{1}{2}$ of £3

6.
$\frac{1}{4}$ of £10 $\frac{1}{3}$ of £9

Now try this!

• **Make up four more money purse puzzles.**
• **Ask a friend to solve them.**
• **Write down the answers before your friend tries them.**

Teachers' note Remind the children to include unit symbols in their answers, i.e. £ or p.

Developing Numeracy
Numbers and the Number System
Year 4
© A & C Black 2000

Fraction frenzy

- **What fraction of the larger shape is the smaller shape?**

Example: $\dfrac{2}{5}$

1. 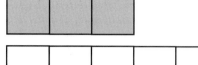 ___

2. 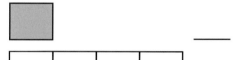 ___

3. 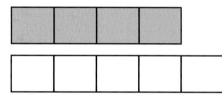 ___

4.  ___

5.  ___

6. 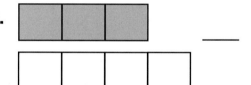 ___

- **What fraction of the larger sack is the smaller sack?**

Example:  $\dfrac{1}{2}$

1. 3 kg 5 kg ___

2. 2 kg 7 kg ___

3. 2 kg 6 kg ___

4. 1 kg 9 kg ___

Teachers' note Children often find this type of fraction work quite difficult; remind them that the larger object or item should be viewed as the whole. As an additional extension activity, the children could make shapes out of Multilink cubes, using different colours for parts of each shape. They could ask each other what fraction of each shape is in each colour.

Developing Numeracy
Numbers and the Number System
Year 4
© A & C Black 2000

Bargain buys

• **List the free items which shoppers receive when they buy:**

1. 2 bags of crisps and 3 packets of biscuits

_____

2. 16 apples and 3 packets of biscuits

_____

3. 4 bags of crisps and 24 apples

_____

4. 6 packets of biscuits and 2 bags of crisps

_____

5. 8 apples and 6 packets of biscuits

_____

6. 4 bags of crisps, 8 apples and 3 packets of biscuits

_____

7. 6 packets of biscuits, 6 bags of crisps and 24 apples

_____

• **Make up special offers for three more items.**
• **Write four different shopping lists for your items.**
• **Ask a friend to work out which items would come free with each shopping list.**
• **Write the answers before your friend tries them.**

Teachers' note The activities on this sheet involve early ideas of proportion. Provide practical materials to help children who need additional support.

Developing Numeracy
Numbers and the Number System
Year 4
© A & C Black 2000

One in every...

- **Colour the scarves in the correct pattern.**

Example: One in every three parts is shaded.

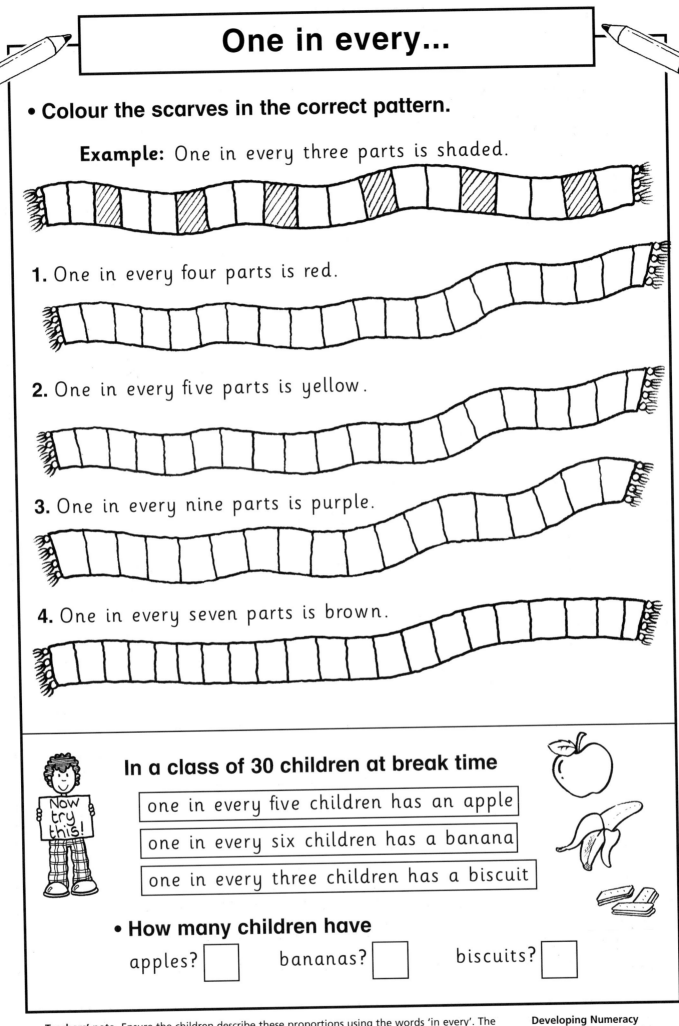

1. One in every four parts is red.

2. One in every five parts is yellow.

3. One in every nine parts is purple.

4. One in every seven parts is brown.

Now try this!

In a class of 30 children at break time

| one in every five children has an apple |
| one in every six children has a banana |
| one in every three children has a biscuit |

- **How many children have**

apples? ☐   bananas? ☐   biscuits? ☐

Teachers' note Ensure the children describe these proportions using the words 'in every'. The terms 'for every' and 'to every' describe the number of parts of one compared with the number of parts of another. This is a different idea from those explained on this sheet, where one part is compared with the whole.

Developing Numeracy
Numbers and the Number System
Year 4
© A & C Black 2000

Decimal birds

• **Write** in words **the value of the underlined digit.**

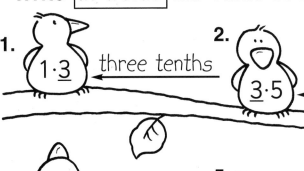

1. 1·<u>3</u> ← three tenths

2. <u>3</u>·5

3. 23·<u>1</u>

4. 10·<u>2</u>

5. 1<u>6</u>·2

6. 0·<u>9</u>

7. 103·<u>41</u>

8. 2<u>7</u>1·6

• **Write these fractions as decimals.**

1. $\frac{7}{10}$ = 0·7

2. $\frac{3}{10}$ = ____

3. $\frac{1}{10}$ = ____

4. $\frac{9}{10}$ = ____

5. four tenths = ☐

6. eight and two tenths = ☐

7. ten and six tenths = ☐

8. one and one tenth = ☐

9. twenty-two and nine tenths = ☐

Now try this!

• **Which is the** largest decimal **on this page?**

• **Which is the** smallest decimal **on this page?**

• **Write all the decimals on this page in order.**

Teachers' note Encourage the children to write these numbers into columns to help them to see the values of the digits.

Developing Numeracy
Numbers and the Number System
Year 4
© A & C Black 2000

What's the difference?

- **Write the difference between the numbers.**
- **Use the number lines to help you.**

1. 2·6 .... 3·7 = __1·1__

2. 13·2 .... 11·9 = ____

3. 6·2 .... 6·9 = ____

4. 17·4 .... 16·2 = ____

5. 8·7 .... 10·4 = ____

6. 5·1 .... 2·7 = ____

- **Count on or back to find the difference between these pairs of numbers.**

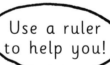
Use a ruler to help you!

7. 5·4 and 7·1 [ ]

8. 6·3 and 4·8 [ ]

9. 10·6 and 11·3 [ ]

10. 4·1 and 2·5 [ ]

11. 8·7 and 10·3 [ ]

12. 12·8 and 9·9 [ ]

13. 0·4 and 3·3 [ ]

14. 6·2 and 3·9 [ ]

Now try this!

- **Write ten pairs of decimal numbers which have a difference of** [0·7].

Teachers' note Encourage the children to check whether the numbers on the number lines are increasing or decreasing. For extra support, the children can use rulers with millimetres marked on them to help them complete the second section.

Developing Numeracy
Numbers and the Number System
Year 4
© A & C Black 2000

• Write these numbers into the correct places on the number lines.

1.

0·8   1·2   0·4   1·1
   0·7   0·3   0·6

0 ————————————————————— 0·8 ————————————————————— 1·6

2.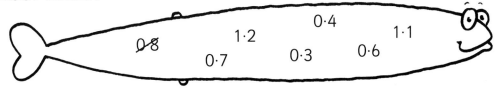

2·7   3·3   3·2
3·5   3·1   3·9   3·0   2·6

2·5 ————————————————————————————————— 4·1

3.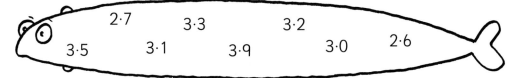

4·7   3·8   4·1   4·5
4·3   3·6   4·0   4·9   3·5   3·9

3·4 ————————————————————————————————— 5·0

4.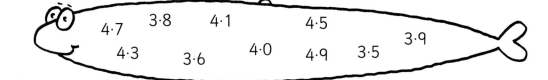

5·5   6·4   5·9   5·7
   6·1   6·7   5·3   6·5

5·2 ————————————————————————————————— 6·8

5.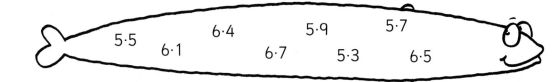

0·6   0·7   1·8   1·3   0·9   1·2
   1·5   2·0   1·9

0·5 ————————————————————————————————— 2·1

• Draw a number line from ⬚0 to ⬚4.
• Write these numbers on the number line.

| 1·2 | 3·5 | 0·8 | 1·7 | 2·9 | 3·1 |

Teachers' note Some children may find it easier to write numbers above every division of the number lines.

Developing Numeracy
Numbers and the Number System
Year 4
© A & C Black 2000

Money, money, money

- **Cut out the cards.**
- **Put the amounts in order, starting with the smallest.**
- **Now pick two cards and write the numbers.**
- **Write an amount that lies between them.**
- **Do this ten times.**

Example: 69p 40p 34p
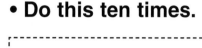

69p	£6.13	£2.15
£4.01	£1.27	£6.89
£6.31	£5.50	34p
£61.83	£3.71	£30.04
£3.64	£3.20	£4.10

Teachers' note Encourage the children to read the prices aloud. The cards can be used to practise adding amounts or to find 'one pound more or less', or '10p more or less', in whole class activities.

Developing Numeracy
Numbers and the Number System
Year 4
© A & C Black 2000

Pounds and pence

• **Write these amounts in** pounds.

1. 375p = £_____   **2.** 414p   = £_____   **3.** 1074p = £_____

4. 603p = £_____   **5.** 773p   = £_____   **6.** 250p = £_____

7. 132p = £_____   **8.** 1817p = £_____   **9.**   99p = £_____

~∿ BANK NOTE ∿~

• **Write these amounts in** pence.

10. £5.78 = _____ p   **11.** £7.16   = _____ p   **12.** £1.91 = _____ p

13. £3.86 = _____ p   **14.** £19.53 = _____ p   **15.** £6.06 = _____ p

16. £4.05 = _____ p   **17.** £24.00 = _____ p   **18.** £0.74 = _____ p

• **Add the coins together.**
• **Write the total amount in** pounds.

19.

 £1   £1   £1   50p   10p   10p   5p   = £_____

20.

£2   £1   10p   10p   2p   2p   1p   = £_____

• **Choose five amounts from the bank note at the top of the page.**
• **Draw coins and notes to show the amounts.**

Example: 1074p = £10·00 50p 20p 2p 2p

Teachers' note As an additional extension activity, give the children a page from a catalogue and ask them to convert the prices from pounds to pence.

Developing Numeracy
Numbers and the Number System
Year 4
© A & C Black 2000

Centimetre centipede!

- **Take turns to roll a dice and move your counter.**
- **When you land on a measurement, convert the metres to** centimetres **.**

Remember, there are 100 centimetres in 1 metre.

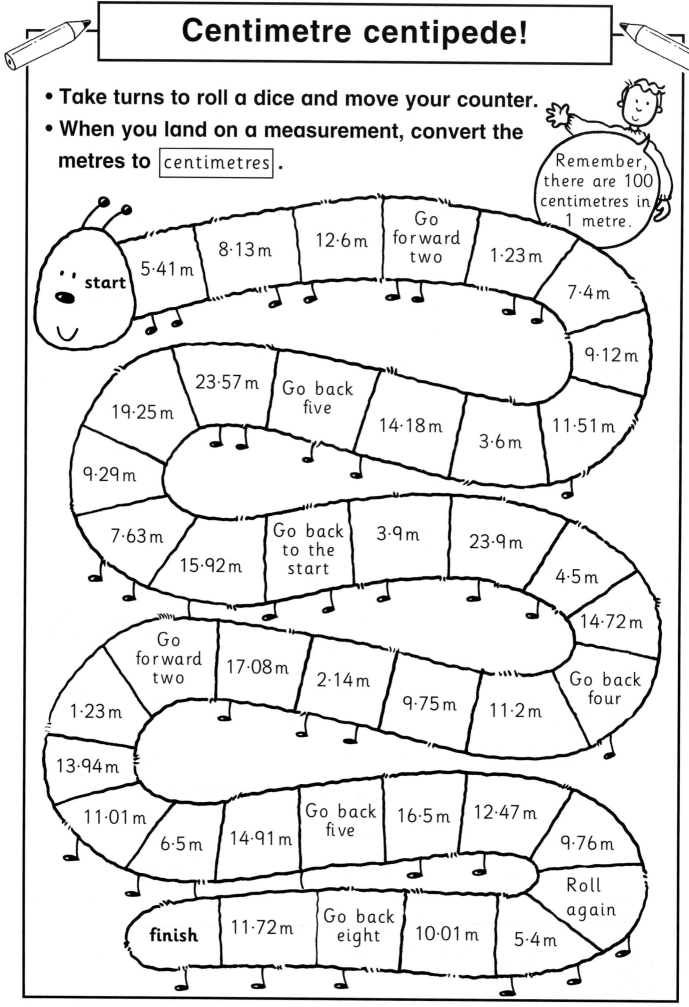

start · 5·41 m · 8·13 m · 12·6 m · Go forward two · 1·23 m · 7·4 m · 9·12 m · 11·51 m · 3·6 m · 14·18 m · Go back five · 23·57 m · 19·25 m · 9·29 m · 7·63 m · 15·92 m · Go back to the start · 3·9 m · 23·9 m · 4·5 m · 14·72 m · Go back four · 11·2 m · 9·75 m · 2·14 m · 17·08 m · Go forward two · 1·23 m · 13·94 m · 11·01 m · 6·5 m · 14·91 m · Go back five · 16·5 m · 12·47 m · 9·76 m · Roll again · 5·4 m · 10·01 m · Go back eight · 11·72 m · finish

Teachers' note This is a game for two to four players. Each group will need a dice and a counter for each player. Encourage the children to write their answers down and check each other's answers as they play.

Developing Numeracy
Numbers and the Number System
Year 4
© A & C Black 2000

The price is right

• **Round the price of each item to the** ⌈nearest pound⌉ .

£18.48

£13.00

£28.00

£18.81

£16.53

£23.00

£17.00

£25.79

£26.64

£29.00

£23.33

£29.14

£14.00

£19.00

£14.27

£18.00

£12.59

£27.00

£26.00

£27.50

• **Round the price of each item to the** ⌈nearest ten pence⌉ .

Now try this!

Teachers' note Remind the children that 50p is normally rounded up to the nearest pound.

Developing Numeracy
Numbers and the Number System
Year 4
© A & C Black 2000

Money puzzles

• **Solve these number problems.**

1. Tom has £3 pocket money. He spends 56p on sweets. How much money does Tom have now? _____

2. Zoe has £4.86. Her mum gives her another 45p. How much money does Zoe have now? _____

3. Hamil buys a pencil for 37p, a rubber for 59p, a ruler for £1.20 and a sharpener for 61p. How much does Hamil spend altogether? _____

4. Ling spends £2.24 and has £1.97 change. How much money did she have to start with? _____

5. A rabbit hops 1.3 m across a bridge and then hops 2·7 m further. How far does it hop altogether? _____

6. A footballer kicks a ball 15·43 m down the pitch. His team-mate kicks it 7·85 m further. How far does the ball travel in total? _____

Now try this!

• **Write four more number problems.**
• **Ask a friend to solve them.**
• **Write the answers before your friend tries them.**

Teachers' note Some children may find the problems too difficult to work out mentally. Encourage them to write down the calculations if necessary.

Developing Numeracy
Numbers and the Number System
Year 4
© A & C Black 2000

Tipping the balance

- Write the numbers on the tins so that the balance scales tilt in the correct direction.

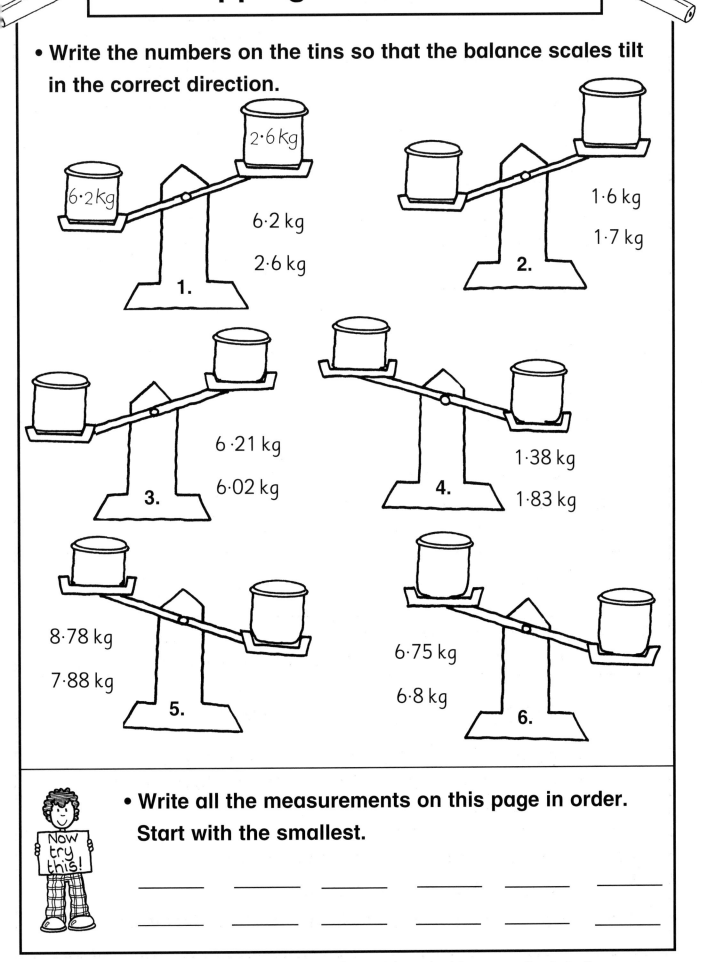

1. 2·6 kg 6·2 kg

6·2 kg

2·6 kg

2. 1·6 kg

1·7 kg

3. 6·21 kg

6·02 kg

4. 1·38 kg

1·83 kg

5. 8·78 kg

7·88 kg

6. 6·75 kg

6·8 kg

- Write all the measurements on this page in order. Start with the smallest.

Now try this!

____ ____ ____ ____ ____ ____

____ ____ ____ ____ ____ ____

Teachers' note A common error made by children is to think that 0.75 is larger that 0.8.

Developing Numeracy
Numbers and the Number System
Year 4
© A & C Black 2000

Rabbits on the loose

• Match equivalent fractions and decimals to work out which rabbit belongs in which hutch.

• Complete the fraction statements using decimals.

Example: $\frac{1}{2}$ of 50 = 0·5 x 50 = 25

1. $\frac{1}{4}$ of 8 = _____ = _____

2. $\frac{3}{4}$ of 12 = _____ = _____

3. $\frac{1}{10}$ of 30 = _____ = _____

4. $\frac{3}{10}$ of 100 = _____ = _____

Teachers' note Explain that the word 'of' in maths can be represented by 'x' (times), for example, $\frac{1}{4}$ of 8 = $\frac{1}{4}$ x 8. Suggest to the children that they use a different colour to join each rabbit to its hutch.

Developing Numeracy
Numbers and the Number System
Year 4
© A & C Black 2000